HIM & HER'S
SMUGGLING
VACATION

WRITTEN & DRAWN
BY
JASON WILSON

CRIME CONSULTANCY
BY
TONY SPENCER

ART ASSISTANCE
BY
TERRY JONES

PUBLISHED
BY
DEALER COMICS

Published by Dealer Comics
Copyright© 2006 by Jason Wilson.

All rights reserved.

The right of Jason Wilson to be identified as the author
of this work has been asserted in accordance
with the Copyright, Designs and Patent Act 1988.

This first edition first published in Great Britain in 2008 by
Dealer Comics.

Printed in Great Britain.

www.smugglingvacation.co.uk

ISBN 978-0-9559170-0-4

VRRRRRR RRRR RRR

MEANWHILE, NOT SO FAR AWAY, ANOTHER ASPECT OF SPANISH TOURISM IS UNDER WAY. AN ABSENT MOON PROVIDES THE NECESSARY DARKNESS FOR SPAIN'S DRUGS TRADE TO THRIVE...

...SPEEDY 'RIB' BOATS, BANNED FROM SPANISH WATERS, MAKE THE RUN FROM MOROCCO TO THEIR PRE-ARRANGED MEETING POINTS ALONG THE SPANISH COAST.

VRRRRRR RRRR

THE BOAT LANDS ON THE BEACH WHERE THE AWAITING GANG JUMP INTO ACTION. FOR THE NEXT TWENTY MINUTES THEY ARE VULNERABLE TO POLICE ATTENTION (THE GUARDIA CIVIL), CUSTOM BOATS AND OF COURSE, THIEVING LOCAL GANGS.

SPLASH

...WORKING AS A TEAM, THEY MOVE THE BAILS OF CANNABIS UP THE BEACH TO THE AWAIT -ING FOUR WHEEL DRIVE VEHICLES WHICH WILL MOVE IT ONTO THE SAFEHOUSE WITHIN MINUTES...

...EXCEPT ON THIS OCCASION...

WHERE THE FUCK ARE THEY?!

!?!

FUCK ME!

BOLLOCKS!

STASH IT AWAY BEHIND THOSE ROCKS BACK THERE. I'LL GET PASTILLE ON THE WALKIE.

RIGHT BLOOMIN COCK UP THIS IS.

WHERE THE FUCK ARE YOU?! WE'RE STUCK HERE WITH THE GEAR AND NO TRANSPORT!!

WE'VE GOT A HOLD UP AT OUR END, NOTHING TOO SERIOUS, BUT WE'VE GOT SPANISH OLD BILL BLOCKIN' THE ROAD DOWN TO YOU...

-WHAT!

SHIT! GUARDIA CIVIL!! FUCK ME!

FUCK THIS! I'VE 'AD ENOUGH OF THIS BOLLOCKS!

SCREW THIS..! -LATER!

-I'M OFF...

TELL THE LADS 'NOT TO PANIC'. I'LL CALL YOU BACK WHEN ALL'S CLEAR. OKAY?

...SO THEY'VE DRAGGED IT TO HERE, THEN THEY'VE STOPPED, AND THEN ONLY ONE THING COULD HAVE HAPPENED...

WHAT'S THAT THEN?

...THEY HOISTED IT UP OF COURSE... MUST HAVE HAD TWO TO THREE HOURS MAX! WOULD'VE TOOK SOME PLANNING.

-BLIMEY!

...THEY MUST HAVE RENTED A ROOM, HAD THE HOIST EQUIPMENT READY...PROBABLY BEEN WATCHING US FOR DAYS.

SO HOW DO WE GET IT BACK THEN?

SO FIRSTLY, WE COUNT HOW MANY BRICKS WE HAVE - RIGHT?

RIGHT!

WE THEN PUT THE BRICKS OUT ON THE BALCONY. IT'LL GET RID OF THE SMELL -RIGHT?

RIGHT!

I THEN GO TO THE RECEPTION AND RING MIKEY FOR SOME ADVICE -RIGHT?

THAT'LL BE MIKEY YOUR BROTHER?

RIGHT!

RIGHT!

HE CAN THEN TELL US HOW TO GET IT BACK TO ENGLAND WITH JNO RISK!

-AND THEN..?

...WELL THAT'S IT MORE OR LESS...

-OH...

WELL..?

...SO BASICALLY, WE, PERHAPS WITH YOUR BROTHER ARE GOING TO BECOME DRUGSMUGGLERS!

WELL.../...
...ER...EM...

...I WOULDN'T PUT IT QUITE LIKE...

- IT'S JUST FOR A COUPLE OF DAYS!

IN A BRITISH PUB, SOME ELEVEN HUNDRED MILES AWAY.

♪ ..BET YOU LOOK GOOD ON THE DANCE FLOOR.. ♪

-YOU GONNA ANSWER THAT?

-C'MON, IT'S IMPORTANT. -DON'T LET ME DOWN. NOT THIS TIME...

WE'LL LEAVE IT AT THAT THEN. AS LONG AS IT DOESN'T HAPPEN AGAIN. -OKAY? -ADIOS SEÑOR.

GRACIOUS SEÑOR. YOU ARE VERY REASONABLE.

...BEST SEE WHO IT IS. -AY, IT MUST BE OUR KID FROM DOWN SPAIN. -GONE WITH THAT BIRD OF HIS.

ALRIGHT BRUV, HOW'S IT GOING? HAS SHE DUMPED YOU YET? ...OKAY...ALRIGHT... -DON'T BE SO SENSITIVE, I'M ONLY JOKING...

-NOW LOOK AND LISTEN, SOMETHING'S CAME UP AND I'M GONNA NEED YOUR HELP ON IT...

ALRIGHT. I'M LISTENING.

A GOOD RESULT. NOW WE CAN TELL PASTILLE, GET TOOLED UP, GO IN AND GRAB IT...

CANNABIS!! -ON A BEACH!! -ARE YOU SERIOUS?!

-SHSHSH! -KEEP IT QUIET!

-OKAY, OKAY... BETWEEN YOU AND ME... RIGHT... ...YEAH... BLIMEY! -OVER A THOUSAND... .....SO WHERE IS IT NOW? ...IN YOUR HOTEL ROOM! -ARE YOU CRAZY?!

THERE WAS NOWHERE ELSE TO PUT IT! NOW IT'S IN THE ROOM, IT'S STINKING THE PLACE OUT -AND FOR ALL I KNOW, SOMEONE SAW US MOVING IT!!

ALRIGHT. OKAY THEN. YOU NEED TO MOVE IT QUICK! RIGHT, HERE'S WHAT TO DO, AND DON'T HANG ABOUT OTHERWISE YOU COULD BE TOTALLY FUCKED UP!!

-SO THESE FOUR BLOKES ARE CHECKING OUT THIS MORNIN'. -I SAY WE GO IN ALL TOOLED UP AND GRAB IT.

-AND IF THEY HAVEN'T GOT IT, SPANISH OLD BILL GET INVOLVED AND WE LOSE THE GEAR.

BETTER IDEA, SMARTIE AND ME'LL WATCH THE OUTSIDE. -YOU, TREBOR AND ROLO GO INSIDE. ONE OF YOU WATCH THE RECEPTION, THE OTHER TWO CHECK THOSE ROOMS OUT. -AS SOON AS THEY TRY TO MOVE IT, WE GO IN HARD AND GRAB IT!!

ENGLAND

DOVER - BRITAIN'S BOOZE CRUISE CAPITAL. BUT ALSO NUMBER ONE PORT FOR EVERY OTHER TYPE OF SMUGGLING.

WHAT'S NEW PUSSYCAT? -WOOOAHH! -WOOAHH!!

HERE WE ARE THEN...NOT BEEN HERE FOR AGES. HASN'T CHANGED MUCH AT ALL.

Welcome to DOVER in White Cliffs Country

MiKEY NEEDS

...HE FOLLOWS HIS OLD ROUTINE. BUYING A HALF DAY RETURN FOR SEVENTY QUID. -HE PAYS CASH OF COURSE.

THERE'S ONE LEAVING IN TEN MINUTES. SHALL I BOOK IT?

DEFINITELY - SPOT ON.

£226 7 DAY

EVEN THE BOOKING AGENT IS UN-AWARE THAT AS SOON AS HIS DE-TAILS ARE TYPED IN, CUSTOMS & EXCISE ARE NOTIFIED...

BUSY TODAY THEN?

JUST PRINTING YOUR TICKET...

TAP! TAP! TAP!

...BY THE TIME HE REACHES THE FERRY, CONCEALED CAMERAS HAVE PHOTOGRAPHED HIM MANY TIMES THE BEST IMAGES ARE FORWARDED TO THE PLAIN CLOTHED OFFICERS ONBOARD.

-THE SUSPECT'S JUST BOARDING NOW...ARRIVED ON HIS OWN...YES SIR, THEY'RE ON STANDBY...

DOVER

WHAT'S NEW PUSSYC

-HE WILL SPEND MUCH OF THE NEXT TWO AND A HALF HOURS CATCHING UP ON THE WORLD OF CURRENT AFFAIRS...

I'VE GOT THE SUN, STAR AND MIRROR. Y'HAVEN'T GOT A 'SPORT' HAVE YOU?

BROWN IS NUTS

WHILST DOWN BELOW HIS VAN, NOW UNATTENDED, IS OPENED UP BY UNDERCOVER OFFICERS WHO PREPARE THE TOOLS OF SURVEILLANCE...

THIS IS IT ALRIGHT.

LET'S OPEN HER UP THEN.

...FIRSTLY, A TRACKING DEVICE (GPS SYSTEM) IS TO BE FITTED.

THIS ALLOWS THE VEHICLE'S MOVEMENTS TO BE TRACKED...

SECONDLY, A VOICE ACTIVATED MICROPHONE IS FITTED TO THE IN-TERIOR TO PICK UP PHONE CONVERSATIONS.

RECEIVER/TRANSMITTER
BATTERY

...WHICH ARE TRANSMITTED TO A FOLLOWING SURV-EILLANCE CAR.

BACK ON LEVEL TWO. MIKEY GRABS SOMETHING RESEMBLING AN ENGLISH BREAKFAST...

-BLOODY RIP OFF THESE PLACES!

THAT'LL BE £12.25 PLEASE. ANY SAUCE?

...THROUGHOUT, HE IS BEING WATCHED BY PLAIN CLOTHED CUSTOMS OFFICERS...

SO TONY BLAIR AND LIONEL BLAIR AREN'T BROTHERS!! -WOW! -THE THINGS YOU LEARN.

THESE OFFICERS ARE NOW PART OF 'OPERATION FOX'. FOR NOW THEY WILL JUST OBSERVE -COLLECTING INFORMATION... -THE ARRESTS WILL COME LATER.

TAP! TAP! TAP!

...SUSPECT ALONE... ...USUAL ACTIVITIES... ...ALL TOO FAMILIAR.

BACK IN THE COSTA DEL SOL, THE DRUGS GANG HAVE REGROUPED WITH PASTILLE JONES RETURNING TO BASE ALONE...

I'VE HAD THE WORST OF MORNINGS, I HAVEN'T EATEN. WOULD YOU DO SOME FOOD?

-WHAT! YOU'RE WANTING ME TO MAKE iT?

-LOOK, I'VE WORK TO DO. GOTTA ORGANISE A SEARCH FOR SOME LOST GEAR. NOW WHILST I GET WORKING ON THAT, I'D LIKE YOU FOR ONCE TO DO ME SOME FOOD...

I'M NOT YOUR SKIVVY! -I DO HAVE THINGS TO DO!

IF I DON'T DO WHAT I DO. YOU CAN'T DO WHAT IT IS YOU THINK YOU DO! SO GET ON WITH IT!

HE CONTINUES TO WORK HIS PHONES USING A BASIC PHONE SYSTEM (FAVOURED BY MANY INTERNATIONAL CRIMINALS) WHICH HE BELIEVES OFFERS CLOSE TO TOTAL PROTECTION FROM POLICE SURVEILLANCE...

SPECIAL ONE TO ONE LINKS JONES TO HIS Nº1 MAN IN THE U.K. -IT'S SWITCHED ON TWENTY FOUR-SEVEN.

TWO MOBILES FOR INCOMING CALLS. -ONE NATIONAL FOR! ALL SPANISH CALLS. -ONE INTERNATIONAL FOR NON-SPANISH CALLS.

NO NEWS? WELL JUST KEEP GOING, SOMETHING WILL HAPPEN SOONER OR LATER. IF THEY'RE TRYING TO GET IT BACK HOME TO ENGLAND, WE'LL FIND 'EM!

U.K CONTACTS

FRANCE

Barcelona
Valencia
Alicante
Murcia

CALL BOXES

TWO MOBILES FOR OUTGOING CALLS. -ONE FOR SPANISH CALLS. -ONE FOR INTERNATIONAL. (Switched on during calls only)

-FOR SECRET CALLS... -MADE FROM CALL-BOX TO CALLBOX. CALLBOX EVIDENCE IS NOT ALLOWED IN A U.K COURT OF LAW.

THERE YOU ARE! AND DON'T SAY I NEVER COOK YOU ANYTHING!

JUST WHAT THE HELL IS THAT SUPPOSED TO BE?

DON'T THINK I'M EATING IT.

SO POLO SMITH HEADS UP THE E902 TO MADRID. NOT THE USUAL ROUTE FOR SMU -GGLING. BUT A POSSIBLE ROUTE TWO AMATEURS MIGHT TAKE...

...I KNOW iT'S A CRAP JOB. BUT IT'S AN IMPORTANT ONE. IT'S A ROUTE THEY MIGHT HAVE TOOK. -I'LL SPEAK TO YOU LATER.

IN   OUT

...OKAY PASTILLE -ANY NEWS AND I'LL RING IN.

TREBOR WITH SMARTIE TAKES THE E15 UP THE SPANISH COAST, THE MOST FAVOURED ROUTE OF COMMERCIAL TRAFFIC AND DRUG SMUGGLERS.

-NO SLOPPINESS TREBOR-THEY'RE MOST LIKELY ON YOUR ROAD. CHECK EVERY SERVICES AND LAYBY AS YOU GO. I'LL CHECK WITH YOU IN AN HOUR.

IN   OUT

...WE WON'T MISS A THING. SPEAK TO YOU IN AN HOUR.

WHILST THE TWO MAIN ROUTES OUT OF SPAIN ARE SEARCHED, ROLO LOCATES THE NEARBY 'DEL SOL RENTALS'...

-IT'S JUST TURNED SIESTA TIME, SO STAY NEARBY. BE READY AS SOON AS THEY OPEN -YOU KNOW WHAT TO SAY. I'LL CHECK IN WITH YOU IN TWO HOURS TIME.

RING TONE!

IT'S TAKEN CARE OF -NO WORRIES.

DEL SOL RE

JONES MONITORS THE SITUATION HOURLY. IN THE MEANTIME HE RETURNS TO THE BUSINESS OF RUNNING HIS DRUG SMUGGLING EMPIRE -THOUGH TODAY HIS MIND IS ELSEWHERE...

-YEAH, DELAYED A DAY OR SO...BIT OF A HOLD UP...WE'LL KEEP COLLECT -ING THE PAPER.*'

...BEING STOLEN FROM HAS RUINED HIS WEEK. ALL THAT HARD WORK FOR NOTHING -THE TIME WASTED, ALL THE DISRUPTION. HE'S NOT JUST ANGRY-HE'S PISSED OFF!

*' PAPER/PAPERWORK= MONEY

ELSEWHERE...

...ISN'T THIS THE MAIN ROAD UP SPAIN...?

ER...YES.

...SHOULDN'T IT BE A LITTLE BIT BUSIER THAN THIS?

WE'RE LOST AREN'T WE?...(sigh)... I THOUGHT YOU SAID YOU COULD READ A MAP?

DON'T HAVE A GO AT ME! -I'VE BEEN DOING MY BEST!! -IT'S NOT MY FAULT.

WELL WHOSE FAULT IS IT IF IT'S NOT YOURS?

-READING IN A CAR MAKES ME FEEL SICK ANYWAY -AND YOU KNOW THAT!

OH, I SEE. MUST BE MY FAULT THEN.

JUST STOP HAVING A GO. WE'LL FIND OUR WAY BACK EVENTUALLY. LET'S JUST ENJOY THE SCENERY.

ALRIGHT. I'M SORRY. -WE'LL JUST WATCH THE SCENERY THEN...

...WE'LL BE ABLE TO ENJOY IT EVEN MORE SOON WHEN WE RUN OUT OF PETROL...

YOU MEAN YOU HAVEN'T PUT ANY PETROL IN?

I THOUGHT THESE THINGS CAME WITH A FULL TANK.

BACK AT THE FERRY, MIKEY ARRIVES AT CALAIS...

HERE WE GO THEN! GET THE MOBY BACK ON, THEN LET'S HAVE SOME MUSIC.

-FOUR CARS BACK, THE SURVEILLANCE CAR FOLLOWS HIM THROUGH THE UNMANNED FRENCH CUSTOMS.

ALL'S GOOD. TRACKER'S WORKING AND TRANSMITTING, BUG IS OKAY I THINK... -SOUNDS LIKE HE'S RUMMAGING AROUND FOR SOMETHING.

...WHERE'S THAT C.D?

CLINK! - CLACK! - "AH, THIS ONE'S GOOD -TOM JONES' GREATEST HITS. YOU CAN'T BEAT A BIT OF OLD TOM...

-NO!

NOT THAT!

29

AT PASTILLE'S DESK...

SO WHAT ARE WE GOING TO DO WITH ALL THESE BLOW UPS THEN?

...WE'RE GOING TO GIVE THE LADS ON THE ROAD A BIT OF A BOOST. -HERE'S WHAT WE'LL DO...

WE TAKE A PICTURE ON THE PHONE WHICH WE TEXT OUT FOR THE LADS TO USE. IT'S THAT SIMPLE!

RIGHT, SO HOW DO WE DO THIS..? ...PRESS THAT... AND THIS ONE... -NOTHING SHOWING..

SUPPOSE TO BE QUITE EASY... -YOU ON THE RIGHT MODE? -I THINK YOU GO INTO PICTURE...

...BOYS AND THEIR TOYS...

JUST OUTSIDE VALENCIA...

WOW! AMAZING... -UNBELIEVABLE. WHO'D'VE THOUGHT?

A MILLION POUNDS. I CAN'T BELIEVE IT. I'M RICH! -I MEAN WE'RE RICH.

A MILLION POUNDS. I CAN'T BELIEVE IT. I'M RICH! -I MEAN WE'RE RICH.

WELL? -WHAT DO YOU THINK ABOUT IT NOW THEN?

I CAN'T GET MY HEAD AROUND IT. A MILLION POUNDS!

NO WONDER THEY WERE SO KEEN TO GET IT ALL BACK.

YOU DON'T THINK THEY'RE STILL LOOKING FOR IT DO YOU?

...AND...? ...NO, THAT'S NOT RIGHT... WE NEED TO GO BACK...

...WHAT YOU DID BEFORE LOOKED RIGHT... PRESS THAT AGAIN.

YOU GO INTO MENU AND PRESS ON CAMERA. -OKAY?

...WITHIN SECONDS.

-AAAH! I SEE. THAT'S WHAT I WAS DOING...

YOU THEN PRESS THAT... -AND THEN IT'S BEEN SENT TO BOTH NUMBERS. THAT'S IT DONE.

THAT'S GONE THEN...

AT MADRID

Beeeep!

FANTASTIC! GOOD STUFF.

JUST OUTSIDE VALENCIA...

Beeeep!

-NOW THAT COULD BE HANDY.

THIS DOESN'T CHANGE THINGS DOES IT?

I DON'T THINK SO -WE'RE GOING TO BE OKAY AREN'T WE?

I GUESS SO. -LET'S NOT THINK ABOUT IT TOO MUCH. SHALL WE GO THEN?

ALRIGHT. -LET'S PAY THE BILL AND GET GOING.

I'LL DRIVE A FEW MORE HOURS. TRY AND GET SOME SLEEP THOUGH.

I'LL TAKE OVER AT BARCELONA REMEMBER TO WAKE ME...

-SIGH...THEY BUY THEIR COFFEE, THEY TALK BUT DON'T DRINK THEIR COFFEE. THEY PAY THE BILL, THEY GO! ...IS SO DEPRESSING.

MEANWHILE, 140km FROM BARCELONA.

WHAT A DAY! SHOULD HAVE BEEN GOING OUT FOR A MEAL TONIGHT... -A FEW DRINKS... PERHAPS A ROMANTIC WALK ALONG THE BEACH...

...INSTEAD OF THAT, WHAT ARE YOU DOING?! ANSWER: DRIVING A VANFULL OF DRUGS ON SOME MOTOR -WAY IN THE MIDDLE OF NOWHERE...

...HERE'S A STRANGE THOUGHT. JUST THINK -AT THIS EXACT MOMENT, NO-ONE IN THE WORLD KNOWS WHERE YOU ARE!! -NO-ONE AT ALL... YOU'RE ALL ALONE...

BUT MAYBE THAT'S ALL ABOUT TO CHANGE...

YEAH PASTILLE, WE'VE **FOUND THEM!** THEY'RE AN HOUR NORTH OF VALENCIA... A WAITER RECOGNISED HIS PICTURE!

GOOD NEWS! NOW PUT YOUR FOOT DOWN. -I'LL GET ONTO POLO. SEE IF HE CAN LINK UP WITH YOU LATER.

POLO! IT'S ME HERE... THEY'VE BEEN SEEN GOING TOWARDS BARCELONA... -TRYING TO GET THE STUFF BACK TO BLIGHTY, HEAD UP AND ALONG THE BORDER AND MEET UP WITH THE OTHERS...

FUCK ME! -I'LL DO MY BEST, BUT I'M FUCKING KNACKERED...I'LL GET GOING THAT WAY BUT IF I BEGIN FALLING ASLEEP I'LL HAVE TO PULL OVER...

OKAY. JUST AS FAST AS YOU CAN...WE'RE GETTING THERE...NOW TO THE NEXT THING, THESE PAPERS YOU GOT...THE RENTAL PAPERS HAVE HIS U.K ADDRESS...

...STANLEY ROBERT JOHNSON 46 RILEY STREET, ALLEYTON. I KNOW THAT TOWN. IT'S NEAR WHERE BROWNIE DELIVERS...I'LL GIVE HIM A CALL.

BROWNIE PRICE, DRUG DEALER AND NIGHTCLUB OWNER. BASED THIRTY MILES AWAY FROM THE TOWN OF ALLEYTON...

ALRIGHT PAL, WHAT'S THE NEWS? YEAH... THAT'S RIGHT... THREE CUSTOMERS THAT WAY. -GIVE ME YOUR INFO AND I'LL MAKE SOME CALLS...

JONE'S PASSES ON THE GATHERED INFO.

CALL ME STRAIGHT AWAY IF YOU GET ANYTHING -OR IF YOU NEED ANY HELP PUTTING PRESSURE ON...

BACK ON THE ROAD...

I HOPE THIS WORKS OUT. I REALLY HOPE THIS IS A GOOD IDEA...

I MEAN IS IT A GOOD IDEA? DO YOU REALLY NEED THIS? ... THINGS ARE GOING WELL ENOUGH AREN'T THEY?

WE'RE OKAY. WE'RE HAPPY. BOTH GOT DECENT JOBS, AN OKAY HOME...A THREE LEGGED CAT. -I MEAN, WHAT MORE COULD YOU ASK FOR?

...THEN AGAIN... IF THIS ALL WORKS OUT... JUST IMAGINE?!

...YOU COULD DUMP THAT CRAPPY JOB OF YOURS AND DO SOMETHING ELSE -SOMETHING YOU LIKE.

...OR WE COULD JUST GO ON HOLIDAY...TRAVEL THE WORLD FOR A YEAR. THAT'D BE GOOD.

THAT'S IF IT ALL GOES WELL THOUGH. BUT THEN, WHAT IF IT ALL GOES WRONG?

MEANWHILE ONE HOUR EARLIER...

- LOOKING FOR INFO ON A GUY CALLED STAN JOHNSON FROM DOWN YOUR WAY... DO YOU KNOW HIM?

STAN JOHNSON? ...NO... 'FRAID I'VE NEVER HEARD OF HIM MATE. -CROSS MY HEART I HAVEN'T.

WELL THINK AGAIN. PEOPLE I'VE SPOKE TO SAY YOU USED TO GO TO SCHOOL WITH HIS BROTHER MIKEY. -HE DRINKS IN ONE OF YOUR LOCALS.

OH HIM, WELL YEAH. I KNOW HIM. -NOT SEEN HIM FOR YEARS THOUGH. WHAT'S IT ALL ABOUT?

HIS YOUNG BROTHER HAS STOLEN SOME GEAR FROM A BIG NAME IN THE SUNNY PLACE*2. I WANT INFO ON HIM AND ANYONE CONNECTED TO HIM. CAN YOU HELP?

HEY, I'LL SEE WHAT I CAN DO. I'LL MAKE SOME CALLS, CALL YOU BACK IN AN HOUR...I'LL DO MY BEST AND GET BACK TO YOU.

AN HOUR PASSES DURING WHICH ROO READS 'HI-FI WEEKLY', AND THEN...

RIGHT. BEST MAKE THIS SOUND GOOD. IN A FEW WEEKS TIME HIS MAN IN SPAIN COULD BE DOING ME A FAVOUR!

- BROWNIE! IT'S ROO HERE. I'VE BEEN ON IT NON STOP. YOU BEST GRAB A PEN, I'VE GOT A SHITLOAD OF INFO FOR YOU...

AND SO THE INFO IS PASSED ON...

-YEAH...I GOT IT ALL...TELL THIS FELLER IT'S APPRECIATED, WE OWE HIM ON THIS.

SO WHAT'S HE COME UP WITH? -WHAT HAVE WE GOT?

JUST ABOUT EVERY-THING WE COULD HAVE ASKED FOR. MAKES IT MUCH EASIER TO SEE WHAT THEY'RE UP TO. HERE'S HOW IT IS...

FIRSTLY, THERE'S AN OLDER BROTHER DRIVING DOWN TO MEET THEM. NAME'S MIKEY JOHNSON AND HE LIVES ON CHURCH STREET IN ALLEYTON, WORKS AS A LOCKSMITH...

-BADA -BADA -DAAAA!

-IT'S NOT UNSUAL TO BE SAD WITH ANYONE!

...THEN THERE'S THE BROTHER WHO NICKED THE GEAR. HE'S CONFIRMED THE ADDRESS AT 46 RILEY STREET WHICH IS A FLAT ABOVE A HAIRSALON - HE'S JUST A NOBODY WHO WORKS IN I.T...

...THEN THERE'S THE GIRL. SHE WORKS IN THE CLOTHING DEPARTMENT AT MARKS AND SPARKS IN ALLEYTON. LIVES WITH THE BOYFRIEND ABOVE THE HAIRSALON...

-AND HER NAME? HERE IT IS -HER NAME IS KAYE BROWN...

*2-"SUNNY PLACE"=SPAIN

WHILST OUR TWO AMATEUR SMUGGLERS DECIDE WHAT TO DO NEXT, WHAT IS HAPPENING ELSEWHERE? - IN NORTHERN SPAIN POLO PASSES THROUGH THE BORDER AT IRÚN...

-THAT WAS STRAIGHTFORWARD THEN...

AT THE VILLA, AWARE THAT THE CHANGING OF SIM CARDS WILL NOT DETER ANY SERIOUS POLICE SURVEILLANCE...

...JONES' AS HE DOES EVERY FORTNIGHT SCRAPS HIS PHONES AND SETS UP A NEW SET.

WHILST HE DOES THIS, ROLO GETS A GOOD NIGHTS SLEEP AT LONG LAST...

SLURP! SLURP!

SLURP! SLURP!

AS FOR PASTILLE'S GIRLFRIEND 'BLINGY', AFTER ANOTHER HARD DAY SHE DESERVEDLY UNWINDS...

HIT ME ONE MORE TIME BABY

AT A HOTEL IN CENTRAL FRANCE, MIKEY'S FRENCH GCSE (GRADE 'E') IS ABOUT TO COME IN HANDY...

AHEM! BONJOUR MONSIEUR. J'AI DIX ANS. J'HABITE...ER ...ERM...CA VA?...JE SUIS ...TIRED...AVEZ...? I-WOULD-LIKE-A-ROOM POR FAVOR?

L'HOTEL BIENTOT

QUOI? VOUS NE PARLEZ PAS FRANCAIS?

SOD IT! LOOK. I AM ENG-LISH. I - SPEAK ENG-LISH.

ENGLISH SUBTITLE WHAT? -YOU DON'T SPEAK FRENCH?

AAH! ANGLAIS. BIEN SUR. VOUS NE PARLEZ PAS UNE AUTRE LANGUE. VOUS ÊTES UN TYPIQUE HOMME DES ÎLES.

AY! WHAT? ERM...I WANT A ROOM... A CHAMBRE! -'SLEEP'.

AAH! ENGLISH. OF COURSE. YOU SPEAK NO OTHER LANGUAGE. YOU ARE TYPICAL ISLANDERS.

(sigh)-IL EST PARTICULEREMENT IGNORANT. JE N'AIME PAS ÊTRE DERANGÉ SI TARD. POURQUOI JE DEMANDE?

C'MON MATE. EIGHTY EUROS; ONE CHAMBRE. WHAT D'YOU SAY? - EH?

THIS ONE IS PARTICULARLY IGNORANT. I CAN BARELY BE BOTHERED AT THIS LATE HOUR. WHY ME I ASK?

WITHIN VIEW OF THE HOTEL...

SO WHAT DO WE DO NOW THEN? WE KNEW THIS MIGHT HAPPEN.

SUPPOSE WE HAVE TO SLEEP OUT HERE FOR THE NIGHT

L'HOTEL BIENTOT

COULDN'T ONE OF US JUST CHECK INTO THE HOTEL FOR THE NIGHT?

CERTAINLY NOT! ANOTHER ENGLISHMAN CHECKING IN AT THIS TIME WILL STAND OUT LIKE A SORE THUMB! NO, WE'RE HERE FOR THE NIGHT. BEST GET THE BLANKETS OUT...

I WOULDN'T MIND, BUT HE HASN'T EVEN SWITCHED HIS C-D OFF!

WHY CAN'T THIS CR

HAD EIGHT HOURS OF THIS SHIT! TURN IT OFF THEN.

HANG ON A MINUTE. ...JUST HEAR THE END OF THIS ONE...

BE MINE

IN THE HOTEL...

JUST BRILLIANT! THEY'RE NOT SO BAD THE FRENCH. JUST PUT EFFORT IN WITH THE LANGUAGE AND THEY APPRECIATE IT...

...SO NOW TO A BIT OF RESEARCH...RIGHT... HERE IT IS...AAAAH! JUST AS I THOUGHT. THAT MAKES SENSE... SEVERAL KILOMETRES APART...

CANNABIS KINGS BY P-A GRATEMER

ALL VERY INTERESTING ...MAKES SENSE. THAT'S THE WAY TO DO IT THEN. ...THEN WE'RE AT CALAIS AND THE MORE DIFFICULT PART.

CANNABIS KINGS BY P-A GRATEMER

...I WONDER HOW THOSE TWO ARE GETTING ON? ...I KNOW. I'LL GIVE 'EM A RING -OH BOLLOCKS! PHONE'S IN THE VAN...I COULD GO OUT AND FETCH IT THOUGH...

NAAHHH! FUCK THAT! THEY'LL BE ALRIGHT GOING THROUGH AT THIS TIME...YEAH... -PIECE OF CAKE!

GULP!

PASSPORTS?

NO SEÑOR.

YOUR HAZARD LIGHTS ARE ON! YOU ARE NOT MOVING. HAVE YOU BROKEN DOWN?

¿ALGÚN PROBLEMA?

OH NO... -NOT AT ALL. I FORGOT TO SWITCH 'EM OFF. SOZ MATE.

JUST HURRY SEÑOR. SUNDAY IS OUR MOST BUSY NIGHT.

IS ALL OKAY?!

FUCK ME! THAT WAS CLOSE...

...TOO CLOSE... -RIGHT THEN, HERE WE GO...

WE'RE GOING TO BE ALRIGHT AREN'T WE?

...YEAH...EVERYTHING'S GOING TO BE FINE BABE...

¡SU PASAPORTE!

THERE YOU GO SEÑOR...

TAN BIEN COMO ESPERABA...DÉJEME QUE LE DIGA ALGO.

SÍ...SÍ...

...WELL?

PULL OVER TO THE LEFT. THERE IS A PROBLEM.

WHAT!

TEN MINUTES LATER.

...I FEEL MUCH SAFER NOW. -DON'T YOU?

SUPPOSE SO...

WE COULD FIND SOMEWHERE TO SETTLE DOWN FOR THE NIGHT COULDN'T WE?

I'LL LOOK OUT FOR A LAYBY OR SOMETHING.

LET'S GO TO A HOTEL. I FEEL LIKE SOME CRACKERS!

CRACKERS! -WHAT NOW?!

DON'T YOU WANT TO?

IT'S NOT THAT. WELL....THERE'S THE STUFF TO LOOK AFTER...AND WE DO HAVE A BROKEN...

OKAY THEN. -I JUST THOUGHT.

...OH...

MIND YOU -PERHAPS IT WOULD BE GOOD IDEA TO...

NO -YOU'RE RIGHT...

WE DO HAVE A BROKEN WINDOW. WE SHOULD STAY WITH THE STUFF.

WE COULD PARK IN FULL VIEW OF OUR HOTEL ROOM SO WE CAN KEEP AN EYE ON...

NO, NO, NO. IT'S NOT WORTH THE RISK TO COME ALL THIS WAY ONLY TO MESS THINGS UP.

...OH WELL, I SUPPOSE YOU'RE RIGHT. -BAD IDEA I GUESS...

WE SLEEP IN THE VAN THEN... -AAAH! PULL OVER HERE, THIS IS ALRIGHT. I'LL GET THE BLANKETS.

I DIDN'T KNOW WE HAD ANY BLANKETS.

I TOOK THE ONES FROM THE HOTEL ROOM -AND SOME TOWELS, OH, AND SOME PILLOWS - WELL YOU NEVER KNOW WHAT YOU MIGHT NEED...

IT'S DESERTED HERE. YOU DON'T THINK WE MIGHT...

NON-NIGHT THEN.

OH! - YEAH. ...NIGHT THEN.

sigh...

- NO CRACKERS TONIGHT THEN.

(43)

OUTSIDE THE BIENTOT HOTEL. SOME ACTIVITY IS OBSERVED BY THE TWO WATCHING OFFICERS ON OPERATION FOX...

SO WHAT'S HE BEEN DOING THEN?

IF YOU'D BEEN AWAKE FOR THE LAST HOUR YOU'D KNOW!

IT'S NOT HELPING THAT WE CAN ONLY SEE PART OF THE VAN. BUT HE'S BEEN OUT HERE FOR AN HOUR, MAKING CALLS, RUMAGING AROUND IN THE BACK OF HIS VAN - LOOKS LIKE HE'S WAITING AROUND FOR SOMEONE.

WHY CAN'T HE JUST GO IN THE VAN FOR HIS CALLS? MIGHT TELL US EVERYTHING. YOU THINK HE'S LINKING UP WITH THE OTHERS THEN?

ONLY THING IT CAN BE... - HOLD ON - HE'S OFF MAKING AN -OTHER CALL NOW...

GOOD NEWS BRUV. FOUND THE JUMP LEADS UNDER MY SEAT. - SO HOW LONG YOU GONNA BE THEN?

...WHAT? YEAH... - HALF HOUR'S OKAY ...OH, HANG ON... MONSIEUR! MONSIEUR!!

... HERE HE COMES... - MUST'VE FINISHED HIS CALL...AAHH- NOW A VAN'S PULLING IN. HE'S TALKING TO THE DRIVER... TELLING HIM WHERE TO GO...

WE'VE GOT OUR LINK UP THEN. NOW, WHILST YOU TAKE OVER THE LAPTOP, I'M GOING THE TOILET BEFORE WE GET GOING.

WHAT! - NOW?

WHILST I'M DOING THIS, GET SOME PICTURES.

GOOD IDEA. IT'S ALL SET UP ISN'T IT?

RIGHT. HERE WE GO THEN... AND NOW LINE UP TO THE CAMERA-PHONE.

VERY GOOD. VERY CLEAR...

CAMERA

NOW THE OFFICER WHILST GATHERING PHOTO EVIDENCE APPEARS TO BE NOTHING OUT OF THE ORDINARY.

...THESE SHOULD LOOK GOOD IN COURT...

...THAT'S HIS PLATE NUMBER.

...AND THE DRIVER'S FACE.

PPSSTT! YOU GET ANY?

YEAH, JUST A FEW. BUT HE'S TURNED THAT VAN AROUND NORTHWARDS. I CAN'T SEE WHAT'S GOING ON NOW...

THE PROBLEM OF A FLAT BATTERY IS SOLVED

BRILLIANT! STARTED FIRST TIME. CHEERS MONSIEUR. MERCI SIL VOUS PLAIT.

SUPER! DU PREMIER COUP! SORTIR UN ANGLAIS DU PÉTRIN...Y'A PAS À DIRE, JE SUIS UN VRAI EUROPÉEN.

DAMN & BLAST! HE'S GETTING READY TO MOVE. PSSTT! OY! HAVE YOU NOT FINISHED YET? - HE'S GOING!

ALRIGHT! I'M GOING AS FAST AS I CAN - NEARLY DONE NOW...

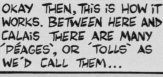

OKAY THEN, THIS IS HOW IT WORKS. BETWEEN HERE AND CALAIS THERE ARE MANY 'PÉAGES', OR 'TOLLS' AS WE'D CALL THEM...

VINGT EUROS S'IL -VOUS PLAT.

VOILA.

QUARANTE EUROS S'IL -VOUS PLAT.

VOILA.

YOU PAY BETWEEN, SAY TEN AND FIFTY EUROS EACH TIME AND GO STRAIGHT THROUGH...

BUT JUST OCCASIONALLY THERE'LL BE FRENCH POLICE ON THESE 'PÉAGES'...

THEY'LL BE LOOKING FOR ALLSORTS: CONCEALED DRUGS, COUNTERFEIT GOODS, ILLEGAL IMM -IGRANTS, GUNS, EVEN BOMB MAKING GEAR.

VOUS ETES DES IMMIGRANTS?

THEY'LL ASK FOR YOUR PASSPORTS AND VEHICLE DOCUMENTS, AND THEN TELL YOU TO OPEN UP THE BOOT. NOW IF THEY DO THAT, THEN WE ARE COMPLETELY FUCKED!

SO TO GET AROUND THIS, I'LL BE IN THE 'LEADCAR' AND BE DRIVING ABOUT SEVEN TO TEN KILOMETRES AHEAD OF YOU PAIR...

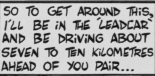

I'M GONNA LIKE THE WAY YOU...

PARIS 260km

-YEAH YOUR MY SEX BUM! AND BABY YOU CAN'T...

WOW! THIS IS GREAT GEAR. FEELS-JUST-

NOW IF I SEE ANY SIGN OF FRENCH POLICE DOING CHECKS AT A PEAJE OR ANYWHERE ELSE! I'LL CALL YOU STRAIGHT AWAY...

EH! FRENCH POLICE! OH BOLLOCKS!

FUCK! GET RID OF THIS QUICK. NOW WHERE'S ME PHONE?

-QUICK BRUV! TURN OFF NOW. OLD BILL'S UP AHEAD!

PEAJE #6

TARGET 1.

ALPHA 1.

YOU THEN TURN OFF A-S-A-P AND GO ON TO THE BACK -ROADS FOR A WHILE UNTIL YOU PASS THE PROBLEM...

-GOTCHA BRUV. TURNING OFF RIGHT NOW.

DON'T YOU KNOW HOW TO ROLL ONE OF THESE?

THEN YOU WORK YOUR WAY BACK TO THE MOTORWAY...

SO WE TURN RIGHT HERE...YES? OY! -ARE YOU READING THAT MAP?

NO, I'M TRYING TO ROLL ONE OF THESE...SHIT! IT KEEPS FALLING OUT...

ONCE BACK, YOU CALL ME AND LET ME KNOW...

YEAH, WE'RE JUST COMING BACK ON NOW. WHERE ARE YOU?

JUST PASSING LE BLANC SERVICES.

AAAH! THINK I'VE GOT IT NOW.

WE THEN USE LANDMARKS AND CLIPBOARDS TO HELP PUT US BACK TO 10KM APART.

JUST PASSING LE BLANC SERVICES.

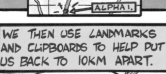

I'M ABOUT SIX MINUTES AHEAD THEN THAT'S ABOUT TEN KILOMETRES. TOP STUFF!

TARGET 1.

ALPHA 1.

AS LONG AS I KEEP AT A GOOD DISTANCE AND BOTH OUR PHONES ARE CLEAR, WE SHOULDN'T HAVE A PROBLEM...

HEY -I'VE DONE ONE. -LOOK AT THAT!

A BIT BIG ISN'T IT?

RIGHT! LET'S LIGHT THIS BABY UP THEN!

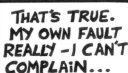

MEANWHILE, TREBOR AND SMARTIE ARRIVE AT CALAIS...

JUST GOING INTO THE PORT AREA NOW...

GOOD WORK. NOW I WANT YOU TO GET NEAR THE TICKET AREA BUT POSITION YOURSELF SO YOU CAN SEE EVERY-ONE COMING IN.

DOING THAT NOW, IT'S TAKEN CARE OF.

-OKAY. I'LL CHECK IN WITH YOU EVERY FORTY FIVE MINUTES.

..AND REMEMBER, STAY OUT OF SIGHT, DON'T DO ANYTHING DAFT, OK? TIMING IS EVERYTHING.

YEAH -THAT'S UNDERSTOOD.

FORTY KILOMETRES BEHIND, POLO MILLS ALSO REC-EIVES HIS ORDERS...

DON'T WORRY PASTILLE... I'M NEARLY THERE.

WELL SLOW DOWN AND FIND A GOOD SPOT TO WATCH THAT MOTORWAY FROM.

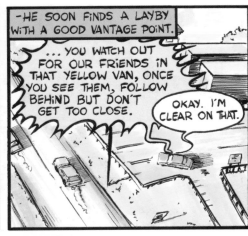

-HE SOON FINDS A LAYBY WITH A GOOD VANTAGE POINT.

... YOU WATCH OUT FOR OUR FRIENDS IN THAT YELLOW VAN, ONCE YOU SEE THEM, FOLLOW BEHIND BUT DON'T GET TOO CLOSE.

OKAY. I'M CLEAR ON THAT.

THEY'RE PROBABLY GETTING THE FERRY BUT IF THEY GO FOR THE TUNNEL, CALL ME STRAIGHT AWAY.

WILL DO MATE -CATCHYA LATER.

AT THAT SAME MOMENT, THE SURVEILLANCE ON OPERATION FOX IS STEPPED UP...

ALPHA 1 -THIS IS BRAVO 2. WE'VE JUST MADE A RECCE OF THE TEN KILOMETRES BE-HIND TARGET 1...

A SECOND CAR JOINS 'OPERATION FOX'. CONTAINING TWO UNDERCOVER OFFICERS SECONDED FROM SCOTLAND YARD'S SO10. THEY BEGIN BY ATTEMPTING TO LOCATE THE GREEN VAN...

WE HAVE A PROBLEM ALPHA 1. WE CANNOT LOCATE THE 'GREEN VAN' -ARE YOU SURE ABOUT THE COLOUR? OVER!

COURSE WE'RE SURE. -OVER!

OKAY, WE'LL TRY AND EYEBALL THE TARGET VEHICLE BEFORE DROPPING OFF. WE'LL DO A RERUN IN MORE DETAIL -OVER!

BLOODY CUZZIES⁶ -BALLS UP ON THE DETAILS EVERY TIME...

ALPHA 1 IS UNIMPRESSED...

THE CHEEK OF THEM. 'TAIL END CHARLIES' TURN-ING UP AT THE ELEVENTH HOUR ASKING STUPID QUESTIONS! -"ARE YOU SURE ON THE COLOUR?"!?

BLOODY UNDER COVER SO10s, THEY THINK EVERYONE ELSE BUT THEMSELVES ARE IDIOTS!

SEX BOMB! SEX BOMB! YOUR MY SEX BOMB AND BABY

BRAVO 2 PASSES THE TARGET VEHICLE WHICH CONTAINS THE MAIN SUSPECT MIKEY JOHNSON.

JUST PASSED THE TARGET VEHICLE. ALL'S AS IT SHOULD BE.

AND BABY YOU CAN TURN ME ON

THEY THEN PULL INTO A LAYBY AND CONTINUE TO OBSERVE AND RECORD ALL THE FOLL-OWING TRAFFIC...

WE'VE FOUR BLUE VANS, FIVE WHITE, ONE RED, NO GREEN AND THIS YELLOW ONE.

ONE OF THEM HAS TO BE IT.

WITH NO GREEN VAN APPEARING, THEY REPEAT THEIR EARLIER 'LEAP FROG' TACTICS.

OKAY ALPHA 1, MAKING A FRESH RUN HERE. BELIEVE EARLIER INFORMATION INCORRECT -OVER!

5 'RECEE'- RECONAISSANCE
6 'CUZZIES'-CUSTOMS & EXCISE

AS THE TRIO APPROACH CALAIS, MIKEY DROPS HIS SPEED DOWN...

OKAY BRUV - YOU SHOULD COME INTO VIEW PRETTY SOON NOW...

NOW IF WE'RE DROPPING OUR SPEED ALSO, THIS COURIER SHOULD PASS US SOON ALSO...

SO IN JUST A FEW MINUTES WE'LL KNOW.

...AND THEN FOLLOW ME, BUT NOT TOO CLOSE.

TARGET 1.

ALPHA 1.

...AND SURE ENOUGH.

YOU THINK THAT'S THEM? 'DEL SOL RENTALS!' -SPANISH PLATES!

I'D PUT MONEY ON IT!

WELL I CAN'T SEE HIM?

HE'S UP HERE SOMEWHERE!

BRAVO 2, YELLOW VAN JUST PASSED US. MALE AND FEMALE - SPANISH NAME AND NUMBER PLATES. HAS TO BE OUR TARGET 2.

WE SAW IT FIRST ALPHA 1 - AND ARE ON TO IT.

DID YOU HEAR THAT? - 'WE SAW IT FIRST'!? - 'AND ARE ONTO IT'! NOT A 'THANKS' OR A 'CHEERS MATE' JUST NOTHING AT ALL. - SO ARROGANT!

THINK THEY'RE STARSKEY AND HUTCH DON'T THEY?

-I CAN SEE YOU NOW. SO JUST FOLLOW CLOSELY BEHIND...

UP AHEAD...

WE'RE GOING TO THE OLD DRINKS PLACE I TOOK YOU TO ONCE - REMEMBER? NOW HAS EITHER OF YOU GOT ANY MONEY ON YOU?

GOT A BIT. KAYE'S GOT HER CREDIT CARD.

DON'T TELL HIM THAT!!

IT'S JUST AROUND THIS CORNER. - I'LL DRIVE IN AND PARK - YOU PULL IN ALONGSIDE ME.

SO WHAT'S THIS PLACE THEN?

YOU NEVER BEEN HERE?

EastEnders

MIKEY NEEDS

- "EASTENDERS - CALAIS' MOST FAMOUS AND PROLIFIC BOOZE WAREHOUSE...

SO ALTOGETHER WE HAVE: 'ME' - 46 EUROS, AND THEN 'BRUV' - 164 EUROS, 'KAYE' - 216 POUNDS + A CREDIT CARD. SPOT ON!

CAN WE ONLY USE THIS CARD AS A LAST RESORT?

SO THE IDEA IS?

YOU SEE THEM?

I SEE THEM.

THE IDEA IS, WE'RE GOING TO BUY ENOUGH BOOZE TO COVER OUR GEAR UP. - SO IF CUSTOMS DO LOOK IN, THEY SEE THE BOOZE AND WITH A LITTLE LUCK WAVE YOU THROUGH.

WHAT DOES HE MEAN - 'WITH A LITTLE LUCK'?

SOUNDS LIKE A GOOD PLAN. LET'S GO.

RIGHT. WE'RE BUYING BIG AND BULKY. THAT MEANS BEERS AND LAGERS - OKAY THEN.

...AND WHAT DOES HE MEAN BY 'WAVE YOU' THROUGH'?! - I THOUGHT HE WAS DRIVING IT THROUGH!

PROBABLY JUST A FIGURE OF SPEECH.

FROM QUITE NEARBY MORE PHOTOGRAPHIC EVIDENCE IS COLLECTED.

...INTERESTING

...EVEN BETTER.

MUST BE LOADING UP WITH SPIRITS TO COVER UP THE CONSIGNMENT. - A TOUCH AMATEURISH.

WE'VE SEEN WORSE.

-45 MINUTES LATER...

WHAT!...£1864.92 - BLIMEY!

HOW ARE YOU PAYING THEN?

C'MON! PAY THE MAN, SIS. - THEN WE CAN GET GOING.

GNRRR! I'LL PAY IT. BUT WE NEED TO TALK!

ONCE WE'RE LOADED UP, WE NEED TO GO THROUGH A FEW THINGS!

BLIMEY BRUV. SHE DON'T HALF MOAN SOMETIMES DON'T SHE?

...SHE HAS HER MOMENTS. RIGHT, KEYS...KEYS! WHERE'S MY KEYS?!

SHORTLY AFTER...

—I CAN'T BELIEVE HE PICKED THAT BLOODY STRAW!!

—FOLLOWING A FEW HUNDRED YARDS BEHIND...

LUCKY SOD I AM. I KNEW TO PICK THAT STRAW. IT WAS OBVIOUS

HE'S GETTIN' ON MY NERVES AL-READY. WHY COULDN'T IT HAVE BEEN HIM?

MINUTES AWAY FROM THE PORT OF CALAIS, THEY BEGIN THE HABIT OF KEEP-ING A DISTANCE FROM EACH OTHER...

CHEER UP SIS, HE'LL BE ALRIGHT. NO WORRIES.

...IT'S ALWAYS THE SAME, HE ALWAYS WINS. ...EVER SINCE WE WERE KIDS.

HEY PASTILLE, IT'S POLO. IT'S JUST PASSED US. THE WIMPY GUY'S DRIVING IT... —YEAH, I'M ONTO IT.

STAN ARRIVES AT THE PORT TWO MINUTES IN FRONT...

...OKAY THEN, TICKETS FIRST, PAY CASH, BE CASUAL...

YEAH, COMING IN RIGHT NOW. HE'LL BE ON THE 19:40 FERRY...YEAH, WE'LL BE ON IT.

...BY THE TIME HE'S BOUGHT HIS TICKET...

THERE YOU GO...

...AND IS DRIVING TOWARDS THE FRENCH CUSTOMS...

HIS PASSPORT DETAILS ARE IMMEDIATELY FORWARDED, HIS NAME HAVING ALREADY BEEN YELLOW FLAGGED ON THE CUSTOMS COMPUTER SYSTEM.

...DETAILS COMPLETE ON STAN ROBERT JOHNSON. STILL AWAITING MICHAEL LIONEL JOHNSON. SHOULD NOT BE LONG NOW.

THE 'YELLOW FLAG' SIGNALS OTHER OFFICERS THAT THE DRIVER IS PART OF AN ON-GOING INVESTIGATION AND IS NOT TO BE DETAINED...

VOTRE PASSEPORT.

VOICI.

ALLEZ-Y!

AH, MERCI.

WELL THAT WAS EASY. COULD BE MY LUCKY DAY AFTER ALL.

FOLLOWING A MINUTE OR TWO BEHIND...

...I'M TELLING YOU, HE MUST'VE GOT THROUGH.

I SHOULD'VE GONE WITH HIM. SHOULD'VE INSISTED. HE'S NOT GOOD UNDER PRESSURE.

AND STILL LISTENING IN...

SO THAT'S THE GIRL'S VOICE THEN, AND SHE'S THE GIRLFRIEND OF THE GUY DRIVING THE DRUGS THROUGH.

THAT'S RIGHT... —KAY BROWN. HAD A CLEAN BACKGROUND —UNTIL NOW THAT IS.

—HE'S FINE UNDER PRESSURE. HE IS A JOHNSON AFTER ALL.

BUT HE'S NOT LIKE YOU. HE'S SENSITIVE.

THE VEHICLES BOARD...

...THERE HE IS JUST DRIVING ON NOW!

THANK GOD. FOR THAT. HE'S FINE, WE'RE FINE, THE GEAR'S FINE.

...TARGET TWO IS NOW ON BOARD. BRAVO 2 WILL CON-TINUE SURVEILLENCE. —OVER.

ALREADY ONBOARD AND ENJOYING THE SEA AIR...

...YEAH, JUST WATCHED THEM COME ON... YEAH, WE'LL BE OFF BEFORE THEM... —YEAH, SWEET.

WE'VE AN HOUR AND A HALF TO KILL THEN LADS. —LET'S HIT THE BAR THEN!

... AND THEN BACK TO WORK AND WE SUPRISE THEM BIGTIME!

THE 19:40 P&O FERRY SETS SAIL FOR DOVER...

HERE WE GO THEN SIS. IN JUST TWO HOURS OR SO WE'LL BE RICH.

...YEAH, WHATEVER. CAN WE GO AND SEE HOW HE IS NOW?

NO CHANCE! WE STICK TO THE PLAN AS AGREED. THESE FERRIES ARE PACKED WITH UNDER-COVER OLD BILL ON THE LOOKOUT FOR ABSOLUTELY ANYTHING.

YOU'RE BEING PARANOID. IT'S NOT GOING TO DO ANY HARM IF WE...

WITH MY BACKGROUND HISTORY I COULD BE ONE OF THE NAMES THEY'RE KEEPING AN EYE ON, WHICH MEANS THEY MIGHT ALSO BE WATCHING YOU...

ME! THEY WOULDN'T BE WATCHING ME -WOULD THEY?

COULD WELL BE... SO WE JUST KEEP HIM ISOLATED -IT BRINGS DOWN HIS RISK. NOW, WHAT DO YOU THINK OF THIS WATCH?

...IT'S BIG, LOUD, DENSE, AND PROBABLY WON'T WORK FOR LONG. IT'S PERFECT FOR YOU!

MEANWHILE, IN THE DOWNSTAIRS BAR...

SO FAR, SO GOOD -YOU'RE DOING WELL. JUST ONE LAST BIT TO GO...

PERHAPS YOUR JUST A LITTLE TENSE THOUGH... MAYBE A DRINK OR TWO WOULD TAKE THE EDGE OFF, MAKE YOU LOOK RELAXED! ...YEAH, THAT'S A GOOD IDEA.

WHISKEY AND COKE PLEASE MATE

FOR AN EXTRA POUND I CAN MAKE THAT A DOUBLE SIR...

YEAH, GO ON THEN.

AND SO...

I'LL JUST NURSE THIS ALONG, TAKE MY TIME.... -GOT TO GET THIS LAST BIT RIGHT.

MIND YOU, I SHOULDN'T BE DOING THIS AT ALL. SHOULD BE MIKEY'S JOB. KAY WAS RIGHT -SHOULD'VE BACKED HER UP ON THAT.

YOU'RE TOO SOFT! THAT'S YOUR PROBLEM. GIVING HIM A CHANCE BY DOING STRAWS! WHAT WERE YOU THINKING?

UP IN FRONT...

SHE'S CHUCKED OUR MIRROR AWAY! WE'VE LOST OUR SOUND! WHAT DO WE DO NOW?

I DON'T KNOW. SHOULD WE RADIO IT IN? WOULDN'T MAKE ANY DIFFERENCE NOW WOULD IT?

SOMETHING THAT WOULD THOUGH...

ESHCUSE ME MATE...AM BIT LATE

OY! WATCH IT MATE!

THE VEHICLES HAVE BEGAN TO DISEMBARK.

HE MUST BE RIGHT AT THE BACK SOMEWHERE. HE'LL BE ALRIGHT ANYWAY. THE ODDS ARE IN HIS FAVOUR.

CONFIRM-WE HAVE LOST SOUND - WILL RETAIN EYEBALL ON TARGET 1. OVER!

YEAH, THATS A POINT. JUST WHAT ARE HIS ODDS?

ODDS?

WHERE THE FUCK IS IT?! AM SURE...hic!...LEFT IT...hic!...HERE...

...I DUNNO REALLY. I'D SAY ABOUT... LET ME THINK...I'D SAY ABOUT ONE IN...AY!-WHAT ARE YOU DOING?

JUST PUTTING YOUR MUSIC ON...

CLICK

NO DON'T DO THAT

SEX-BOMB SEX-BOMB -YOUR MY SEXBOMB!

OH-MY-GOD! WHAT THE HELL IS THAT YOU'VE BEEN...

OH...OH THAT! ...I DUNNO...ER... I GOT IT CHEAP -A QUID IN FACT. JUST GOT IT FOR A LAUGH REA

...SO HOW COME SOME OF THE TRACKS HAVE BEEN UNDERLINED IN THICK RED PEN? -IF I DIDN'T KNOW BETTER I'D...

...AND BABY YOU CAN TURN ME ON

LET'S JUST TURN IT OFF, PUT SOMETHING ELSE ON... -THERE'S SOME ARCTIC MONKEYS THERE, THATS WHAT I USUALLY HAVE ON...

WELL I CAN'T FIND IT... HAVE TO LEAVE THIS ON I SUPPOSE. I'LL TURN IT RIGHT DOWN THOUGH. NOW BACK TO WHAT I WAS ASKING...

OH - OH THAT. WHAT ARE HIS ODDS OF BEING PULLED IN FOR A CHECK..? ERM...YEAH...I'D SAY... ERM .....

C'MON, SPIT IT OUT THEN. BE STRAIGHT; NO MESSIN'. DON'T SUGAR -COAT IT. JUST TELL ME! WHAT ARE HIS CHANCES..?

...BRAVO 2, WHERE IS OUR TARGET 2?

BRAVO 2 TO BASE. TARGET 2 IS STRUGGLING TO FIND HIS KEYS AND IS TRYING TO CLIMB INTO HIS VEHICLE - BELIEVE TARGET 2 IS A LITTLE PISSED!

OKAY BRAVO 2. IS TARGET 2 MOVING THOUGH?

TARGET 2 IS NOW MOVING. IS ABOUT A DOZEN VEHICLES BEHIND US TOWARDS THE STERN. WILL BE DIFFICULT FOR US TO CONTINUE EYEBALLING-OVER!

PHEW! NOW THAT WAS WORRYING FOR A MINUTE OR SO...

...BUT NOW I'M ON THE BALL. I'M THINKING POSITIVE AND FEELING LUCKY. WHATSMORE MY INSTINCTS SAY I'M GONNA GO THROUGH THESE CUSTOMS LIKE A KNIFE THROUGH BUTTER..

SCREACH

BACK AT THE FERRY, TEN MINUTES BEFORE...

...WELL THIS IS A NEW ONE ON ME BRUV!

I MEAN...I CAN UNDERSTAND SOMEONE NICKING OUR VAN -BUT SWAPPING IT!!!

IT'S A NEW ONE ON ME TOO TEL BOY...

...AND ANOTHER THING. THIS ONE'S MUCH BETTER THAN OURS, ALL SHINY AND THAT - AND I BET IT'S FULL OF BOOZE.

SO WHAT DO WE DO WITH IT?

WE SHOULD REPORT IT TEL!

NO WE SHOULDN'T. WE SHOULD HOT WIRE IT! -GRANDAD-OVER TO THE DRIVER'S SIDE AND TAKE A LOOK. TOBY! YOU CHECK THE BACK...

ARE YOU SURE WE SHOULD...

AND SO...

BUT I DON'T KNOW ANYTHING ABOUT WIRING A CAR TEL -BOY...

I THOUGHT YOU SAID BEFORE THAT YOU USED TO WORK WITH...

OY!-TEL! THEY'VE BOUGHT LOADS MORE BOOZE THAN US...sniff...sniff...

AY, AND YOU'LL NEVER GUESS WHAT I'VE FOUND IN THE BACK OF THE VAN?

LOVELY JUBBLY! RIGHT. YOU'RE IN THE BACK GRANDAD.

BUT I'M ALWAYS IN THE BACK TEL BOY.

SO I'M DRIVING THEN AM I?

ONE MINUTE LATER...

WHAYHAY! -WE'RE OFF. NOW TAKE IT EASY WITH THEM GEARS TOBY...

-ALRIGHT! IT'S A LEFT HAND DRIVE INNIT? AM I NOT USED TO IT AM I...?

WE'VE DONE WELL HERE BRUV. WE'LL GIVE IT A RESPRAY WHEN WE GET HOME - CHANGE THE NUMBER PLATE - FLOG ALL THAT BOOZE...

LET'S JUST GET OUT OF HERE FIRST SHALL WE, AY? WE'VE CUSTOMS UP AHEAD.

-HOWEVER...

BIT QUIET TODAY INNIT? NOT ON STRIKE AGAIN ARE THEY?

THEY'LL BE ON TEABREAK - IN THE OFFICE SUPPING TEA...

...sniff...sniff... HEY TEL, -CAN YOU SMELL THAT? -THERE'S A FUNNY SMELL COMING FROM THE BACK!

GRANDAD!! I'VE TOLD YOU ABOUT THAT BEFORE...

IT'S NOT ME TEL-BOY, IT'S COMING FROM THESE CRATES AND BOXES...

HEY TEL, I'VE SMELT THAT SMELL SOMEWHERE BEFORE...

71

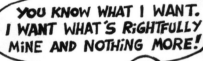